Science Fact or Science Fiction?

Answering children's science questions at Key Stage 2

John Stringer

QUESTIONS
PUBLISHING

First published in 2000
by The Questions Publishing Company Ltd
27 Frederick Street, Birmingham B1 3HH

© John Stringer

Edited by Diane Parkin
Designed by Al Stewart
Illustrations by Sue Woollatt, Graham-Cameron Illustration
Cover design by Lisa Martin

ISBN: 1-84190-024-7

Activities in this book have been selected with care, but safety advice must be followed. Neither the author nor the publisher shall be liable for injuries that may be caused by not following the instructions.

Also available from The Questions Publishing Company Ltd:

Science Fact or Science Fiction?
Answering children's science questions at key stage 1

ISBN: 1-84190-024-9

Contents

Science fact and science fiction

Children's questions

Finding out what children know

How do you teach science? Most primary teachers when questioned are happy to say that they enjoy teaching science. They like its practical nature, the way it excites and motivates children, and its relationship to real life. But they also fear its unpredictability and the apparently superior knowledge of some of the children they teach.

In recent years they have been encouraged to 'start with children's ideas'. This approach (sometimes called constructivism) assumes quite rightly that children do not start out devoid of ideas about the world around them. To teach them science without taking these prior ideas into account is like putting away a coat without a clothes hook – there is nothing to hang it onto.

So teachers have been finding out what their children know before starting their science lessons.

Constructivism

There is nothing new in this. Teachers instinctively pick up the reins, whether it's with 'What do you remember from last time?' or 'What do you already know about …?'.

Constructivism asks that you determine what the children know by observation and related questioning. Simply asking the children what they thought of a particular phenomenon (what happens to salt in water, for example) will get some answers. Many of them will be from children who sincerely want to please you with an answer, any answer, about a topic to which they may never have given a moment's thought. To do it without practical experience denies them the chance to give a reasoned answer.

To get the most informative answers, you are best to let the children have practical experience of dissolving salt in water. As they observe, ask them to explain what they think is going on. Chances are that some will think the salt has simply disappeared. If they use the word 'dissolved' then this may be without real understanding. They may use the word 'melted' which is not what is happening in this case.

Challenging children's thinking

You might ask the children to try the water. What can they taste? Has the water disappeared? Or is it still there, albeit in a different form?

From these ideas you get your general starting point. The first problem may be the range of understanding from those for whom dissolving is a novelty to those who can describe it in molecular terms. Constructivism often leads to differentiation.

But there is another issue. You may be tempted to encourage the children to explain their understanding in depth. This may not be altogether a good thing. Prejudice is not eliminated by constant repetition, and analysing and clarifying their own ideas may actually lead to reinforcement.

What this book aims to do is alert you to the common misunderstandings of children, and adults. Then it offers you opportunities to challenge that thinking in ways that should stimulate without undermining.

The science fact/science fiction approach

This book assumes that:

* Children have their own ideas about the way the world works. They express these ideas by the way they do simple practical tasks, and what they say as they do them. Good, open questioning is important to elicit these ideas.

* Asking children to develop these ideas further may reinforce them. Instead, wrong ideas should be challenged with sensitivity and respect. They should be encouraged to ask questions.

* Many of the questions children ask will not be expressed in words, but will be apparent through their practical activities and drawings.

* Before we challenge the ideas of children, we must be clear in our own minds what **The accepted science** explanation is. Otherwise we shall only sow confusion.

* **The accepted science** explanation is reliable, but not set in stone. Science explanations develop and change as our understanding of the world increases.

With all that in mind, the first question to ask yourself is:

How much do you know?

Before you read any further, answer these questions from your own knowledge and understanding:

1 Trees are big things. When we cut them down we find that they are made up of a lot of wood. But where did all that wood come from? What were the raw materials? How was it made?

2 If you cool a liquid, it will become solid and that solid will be smaller than the liquid it came from. So why does frozen milk push the top off the bottle?

3 Is the dark side of the Moon really dark?

We have our own ideas

We all have our own ideas of the way the world works. Children are no exception. Much recent research has been devoted to understanding children's ideas about the way the world works. This constructivist research has led us to a clearer understanding of the way children think. And it has led to a style of teaching science to young children that begins by challenging their prior ideas.

This approach can be effective in changing children's thinking so it is closer to the accepted scientific explanation. You might say, 'so that it is closer to the truth', but that is to assume that we know the truth – and it would be fair to say that scientific understanding is always developing with new explanations of what we originally believed we all understood. Nevertheless, there are explanations that are nearer right than others and these explanations stand up to scientific scrutiny and rigorous testing.

Teaching to what children already know is both sensible and practical. But it can be undermined by the simple fact that many teachers have their own prior ideas about the way the world works – and sometimes these ideas do not match the accepted scientific explanation either. There is no shame in this. Lewis Wolpert, a professor of science, has argued that science is not about common sense. If you want to understand science, he says, leave your common sense at the door. Most primary teachers survive by common sense. Tough. It is no use to you in science. In fact, if you give a child a common sense answer, you are probably wrong.

Take our three starter questions. What were your answers?

1 Trees are big things. When we cut them down we find that they are made up of a lot of wood. But where did all that wood come from? What were the raw materials? How was it made?

If your answer was that the tree somehow sucked all that material from the ground, then you have to explain why trees aren't standing in great big holes. No, the tree, all its leaves, its trunk, branches, flowers and fruit, were all once water and carbon dioxide. By a miraculous process we call photosynthesis the tree (and other green plants) harnessed the energy of the sun to convert these raw materials to both its structure and the energy it needs to live. (And incidentally, poured oxygen into the atmosphere that you and I need to breathe and live.) Sure, it uses tiny amounts of mineral salts, and we may give it extra, misleadingly calling this plant food'

The lesson? Expect the unexpected.

2 If you cool a liquid, it will become solid and that solid will be smaller than the liquid it came from. So why does frozen milk push the top off the bottle?

Right. If molten metals cool they become solids that take up less space than they did as a solid. The same is true of other materials that exist in both solid and liquid forms. But water – the most abundant liquid on the planet – breaks the rules. Ice cubes are larger than the water they were made from. Frozen coolant can break a car's engine block. And milk – which is mostly water – will expand out of a bottle and force off the cap.

Good thing too. Because it is bigger and less dense than water, ice floats. If it didn't ponds would freeze up from the bottom and there would be no fish in them. Even more importantly, there would never have been life on Earth as we know it. Life originally evolved in the water. And even if it had begun to develop, it would have had to survive periodic freezing, or maybe being brained by sinking ice cubes.

The lesson? The best rules can be broken.

3 Is the dark side of the Moon really dark?

No it isn't. There are times each month when the Moon is only slightly lit on the face – the side that constantly faces us. On these occasions the other side of the Moon is in sunlight. The dark side is light. The word is inaccurate.

The lesson? Don't trust the words we use.

Still with me? Then it's time to try applying all this. Turn to *How to use this book*.

How to use this book

The book is divided into units, each one referenced to the National Curriculum for Science 2000. There are 17 units at Key Stage 1. There are 19 in the **Key Stage 2** book.

Each unit is titled by a common question or misconception. Then sections follow that enable you to challenge children's thinking and work towards the learning outcome.

This is the structure of each page:

Science fact or science fiction?

Title

Key Stage 2

National Curriculum reference: This is to the new National Curriculum for Science 2000.

What children may think

A few lines cannot do justice to the research of the constructivist projects, which include CLiS (Children's Learning in Science) and SPACE (Science Processes and Concepts Exploration). These should be read for themselves.

This paragraph aims to give you a sense of the kind of prior ideas that children may have. Challenging those ideas may demonstrate to you how tenaciously they are held.

What you may think

Most of us have our own prior ideas on science, made up of incompletely understood school experiences, popular science and rationalisations. For examples of this, see the Oxford University PSTS (Primary School Teachers and Science) project. This paragraph may challenge your own thinking.

The accepted science

This section presents the commonly held views, defines a few terms, and reminds you of some of the conventions of science.

The photocopy sheets

Each unit has two photocopiable resource sheets which you may choose to use – in whole or in part – or to modify to your children's needs. Some are practical, some pencil and paper. Where appropriate, answers are given.

Some more activities

This section lists other activities that you could call into play in your teaching.

Learning outcomes

This section lists what most children should know and understand following your teaching, in 'Childspeak' form.

Part 1

Sc1 Scientific enquiry.

1   How do I make this test fair?

Key Stage 2
National Curriculu[m]
reference: Sc1, 2e

What children may think

There are so many apocryphal stories about children and fairness that it's hard to know where to begin. The classic is the answer to the question 'Is it a fair test?'. 'Yes, it's fair. We are all having a go.'

What you may think

'It's very difficult to structure a fair test in the classroom. There are so many factors to juggle. And even if I manage it in the physical sciences, I can't do the same in biology'.

The accepted science

A fair test is one where you can answer three questions:

* What am I going to change?
* What am I going to observe or measure?
* What am I going to keep the same?

Apply this to a simple question like 'Where will an ice cube melt fastest?'.

What am I going to change?	The place I put each ice cube.
What am I going to observe or measure?	How long before each has gone.
What am I going to keep the same?	The size of each ice cube to start with.

Since it's very hard to make changes in biology – you can't pull a spider's legs off to see how it runs – you are more likely to make long term observations of natural changes: what seeds itself in the newly-dug garden bed?

The photocopy sheets

1 Jelly making. Children are asked to find a way of dissolving jelly cubes quickly. (Note – in warm water, jelly cubes melt as well as dissolve; they change state as well as dispersing through water.) They are asked to change one factor; they could:

* change the colour of the cube;
* cut the cube into smaller pieces;
* use warmer water;
* stir the water;
* use a different cup;
* use a different amount of water – or jelly.

They are likely to conclude that cutting up the cube, using warmer water or stirring speeds up dissolving. They should review how good their test was. Would they recommend it?

2 The strongest tube. A paper tube will hold a surprising number of books – paper resists compression well. The tubes must be broad and stable, and loosely held in place by the elastic band. Children might use two or more sheets of paper, or double the tube thickness by folding or make the tube narrower or wider. These changes make some difference, though not a great deal.

Some more activities

You can apply this technique – change one factor and observe the outcome – to many investigations, but not all. Scientific enquiry includes long term observation and sampling – among other techniques – as ways of obtaining evidence.

Learning outcomes

Know that only one factor should be changed (while keeping the others the same) in order to perform a fair test.

Jelly making

Urgent message: the boss wants jelly – quick.
Don't ask me why. Just find a rapid way of
dissolving jelly.

What you need
some jelly cubes;
some plastic cups – transparent are
best for this;
some plastic spoons;
scissors;
water from the tap – warm and cold.
SAFETY! DO NOT use hot water.

Planning
My way of dissolving jelly cubes as quickly as possible:

The change I will make:

I must keep these the same:

The strongest tube

Just how strong is a paper tube?
Prepare to be amazed!

What you need

some scrap A4 paper;
some elastic bands;
some books.

Planning

Roll a sheet of paper into a tube and hold it in that shape with an elastic band. Now stand it on end. Put books on the tube, carefully. Count the books. It will hold a surprising number. But can you improve on that number, by changing the way you make the tube?

Doing

Change your tube. You might change its shape, its height, its thickness, or the materials you use. Only change one factor at a time. Compare your changed tube with the first one you made.

The tube I used:	The number of books it held:

Reviewing

What have you found out?
How good was your evidence?
What would you do another time?

2 Are you really safe?

What children may think

Candles may make you think of your worst nightmare. There's that group at the back of the class ... 'Cor, this is good. Candles! Course, we weren't allowed to light them but they don't half burn! I wonder what will happen if I put this bit of paper in the flame. Look at that! I've got a bigger bit here ...'

What you may think

It's safest if they do as they're told. I know best. And it stands to reason they'll be safest if they follow my rules.

The accepted science

The National Curriculum follows a sensible developmental path in science safety. At KS1, children are expected to recognise hazards and risks when carrying out an enquiry; at KS2, they are expected to recognise those hazards to themselves and to others.

This change from passivity to active learning is important because it gives children transferable experiences and learning that they are unlikely to get if they are simply told about risks without discussion.

But you need advice too.

There is one incomparable publication: Be Safe! the ASE guide to safety in primary science. Be Safe! is published at around £5.00 by the ASE, telephone 01707 283000.

The photocopy sheets

1 Spot the dangers. Children are asked to ring and explain the dangers that they see in the pictures. These show:

* a girl with long, loose hair leaning forward over a lit candle;
* a boy pouring boiling water from a kettle into a plastic cup he is holding;
* a girl looking directly at the Sun;
* a boy mixing chemicals while holding a half-eaten sandwich in the other hand.

2 Make them safe. The same pictures as 'Spot the dangers'. This time pupils are asked to suggest ways of making the activity safe. They could respond verbally or in writing.

Some more activities

Before every science enquiry, KS2 pupils must stop and consider the dangers with you – to themselves and to others – and suggest ways of alleviating those dangers.

Learning outcomes

Know that it is important to assess any risks to themselves and to others before undertaking an enquiry.

Spot the dangers
Are you careful?
Do you think ahead?
Part of being safe is spotting dangers!

What you need
This sheet and a pencil

What to do
Look carefully at the pictures.
Put a ring round each danger.
Explain the danger in
your own words.

Make them safe

What are they up to?
Don't they know that's dangerous?
Tell them, quick – before something happens!

Make them safe
What you will need
This sheet and a pencil.

What to do
Look at these pictures.
Imagine the person in each picture was your friend.
What would you tell them about doing their science safely?

3 How do you recognise patterns?

Key Stage 2
National Curriculur
reference: Sc1, 4a, ·

What children may think

What are patterns? Children will have come across the word already. They may think that patterns are pictures on wallpapers, or bits of paper you use when you are cutting up fabric. They are things you draw or colour. They are nothing to do with science.

What you may think

It's very hard to spot patterns. Just when you think you have a graph that shows a really neat pattern, you get results that buck the trend.

The accepted science

Often, quirky results are due to errors in good practice. It can be that children have wildly misjudged the parameters of an investigation:

* adding far too much sugar to the water to ever get it to dissolve;
* over-watering the plant;
* not dropping the parachute far enough to really see any differences.

Sometimes they are due to errors in recording. Repeat readings can help stamp out these. Thus the distance a car ran down the ramp may be wrongly measured; or because it hit the wall and came to a stop, not measured at the right point.

Don't expect perfection, but look for general trends and remember that it is important to compare what happened with what was expected, closing the loop. You may not always be able to explain your results. You'll find that you end up with a lot of unanswered questions, of course – but that's science.

The photocopy sheets

1 Peter's investigation: The children are asked to find a pattern in an investigation into sound fading with distance.

Is there a pattern to Peter's results? Complete this sentence:

The further you get from a sound source, *the quieter the sound/the harder it is to hear.*

2 Patterns in light: A shady corner is needed for this activity. The children will find that:

* the higher the torch, the shorter the shadow;
* the lower the torch, the longer the shadow.

You can relate this to shadow length through the day.

Some more activities

Any activity that presents a consistent pattern is fine – and that means most of the practical activities in primary science. Tell the children to look out for inconsistencies – which can usually be explained by inaccurate measuring or recording.

Learning outcomes

Learn to recognise trends in the results of investigations and to compare them with their predictions.

Peter's investigation

Do you know when you see a pattern?
Is it just something in the wallpaper?
Or can there be patterns in numbers – and results?

What you will need
This sheet and a pencil.

What to do
Peter had been investigating sound.
He put some cones across the playground – every ten steps.
He asked his friend to play a radio by the first cone.
Then he walked away.
He stopped at every cone and listened.
Here are his results:

How far from the radio	What could I hear
Ten steps	Really loud - heard every word.
Twenty steps	Not so loud. Still hear every word.
Thirty steps	Still hear it. Getting quieter.
Forty steps	Miss some words.
Fifty steps	Can't hear it at all.

What to record
Draw Peter's investigation.
Explain Peter's results.
What is happening?

Is there a pattern to Peter's results?
Complete this sentence: The further you get from a sound source,

....

....

....

....

Patterns in light

*Can you find patterns in your own results? Can
you spot it when you see a pattern?
And can you guess what will come next?*

What you will need
*A torch.
A pencil.
Some Blu-tack.
A large sheet of white paper.
A dark corner.*

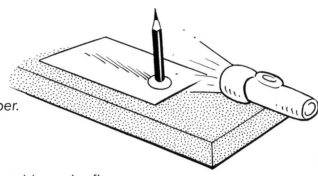

What to do
*Put the white paper on the table or the floor.
Use the blu-tack to fix the pencil upright on the edge of the paper.
Switch on the torch and hold it so that you cast a shadow of the
pencil across the paper.*

*Lift the torch up.
Lower the torch down.
Watch the shadow.*

What to record
Is there a pattern to your results?

*If there is, you can complete these two sentences using the words
higher, lower, longer, shorter:*

The _____ the torch, the _____ the shadow.

The _____ the torch, the _____ the shadow.

*Were there results that did not fit your pattern?
Can you explain them?*

4 How good was your test?

Key Stage 2
National Curriculum
reference: Sc1, 4e

What children may think

Just when we though it was all over, here's something else to do. Not satisfied with getting us to explain our results AND compare them with our guesses, she wants us to tell her how good we think we are. How do we know? Isn't she supposed to be doing the marking?

What you may think

This just adds to the task. What's the point of going all the way through the enquiry again?

The accepted science

The curriculum asks that pupils 'review their work and consider any limitations to their evidence'.

First, remember that evidence is what it's all about. 'I think' should be replaced with 'I know'. But that is not always possible. Take a simple investigation into the minibeasts in the school garden. You might conclude that woodlice are found in damp, dark places from your study of the garden. But that does not necessarily mean that you can extrapolate your results to other gardens and other circumstances. You can make a good guess from your study, but your sample is very small, and you might find conflicting evidence in another habitat.

It's important not to doubt everything, but also vital not to leap from a result to a law.

The photocopy sheets

1 Davina's disaster: There are four things that Davina does wrong. Her results will not be reliable – her evidence is not good enough.

She should use the same plane from the same distance thrown in the same way – and accept it when it doesn't land in the hoop.

2 Conductors and insulators: The children are asked to score themselves in a simple practical investigation out of ten. Then they are asked to justify their score.

Some more activities

In any activity, children could be asked to assess their own work at the end; to evaluate their results and their evidence.

Learning outcomes

Know what makes good evidence and that evidence is not always irrefutable.

Davina's disaster

What you will need
This sheet and a pencil.

What to do
Davina was investigating how model aeroplanes flew.
I'll keep the same aeroplane, she thought.
But bend it different ways. I'll see if
I can get it to land in a hoop.
She had a practice. That was fine.
It landed in the hoop every time.
'Right,' said Davina. 'Now to start.'

With the wings bent, the aeroplane
wouldn't land in the hoop.
So she went a bit closer.
One landed so far from the hoop
that she kicked it in.
She lost her aeroplane.
So she made a new, bigger one.
She hadn't written her results down.
So she made them up at the end.

What to record
How good was Davina's test?
List three things she should not have done.
Tell her how to do her test properly.

Conductors and insulators

Try a test yourself.
Then see how good you were!

What you will need
A battery, bulb and wires linked up in an 'open' circuit - if you touch the two ends of the wire together, the bulb should light.
Some objects to test.
Do not use watches or any electrical device.

What to do
Put the objects in the circuit one by one.
Watch to see if the bulb lights up.
Sort your objects into 'conductors' and 'insulators'.

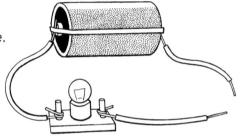

What to record
How good was your test?
Give yourself a score out of ten.

Why did you give yourself that score?

I think I did these things well:

I think I could do these things better:

Part 2

Sc2 Life processes and living things.

5   What do plants eat?

Key Stage 2
National Curriculum
reference: Sc2, 3b

What children may think

Plants draw their food from the soil. See Science fact, science fiction Key Stage 1, Unit 7. 'Photosynthesis' is a magic substance that somehow adds stuff to the plant. Sunlight is another material in all this, and is added to the photosynthesis, air and water. The plant doesn't release energy - it doesn't need energy - it doesn't do anything.

Plants grown in the dark grow better - they are much longer than plants grown on the windowsill.

What you may think

Even adults have difficulty with the concept of photosynthesis. The idea that two tasteless, odourless substances - an invisible gas and the commonest liquid in the world, carbon dioxide and water - are somehow combined to make the basis of our food, our clothing, our furniture and even some of our shelter - seems so improbable as to be impossible.

The idea that we can affect this strange activity in any way seems unlikely.

The accepted science

Photosynthesis is a chemical process like any other. So it is affected by the conditions in which it takes place. In warm conditions, it will happen faster - a good reason for having a greenhouse.

It can only take place in the light. So plants grown in the dark etiolate - they put on a spurt in an effort to find the light. This would work fine if they were under the ground. Eventually they would burst through the soil into the sunlight. Not such a good strategy in the cupboard - but they can't know that.

The photocopy sheets

1 Feeding the plants. This asks the children to choose the correct answer (Debra's) and to advise the other children that water, light and warmth are needed for plants to grow.

2 Growing beansprouts. These are easily grown as described, and make a pleasant change from cress seeds. They also have the advantage of being edible. The children can record the growth, and how the sprouts become green when exposed to sunlight.

Some more activities

Any plant-growing activity is appropriate. Growing food plants adds to the reward. Growing for a date or event enables you to manipulate the speed with which the plants grow. Plants can be chosen from a range of cultures.

Learning outcomes

Know that the leaf produces new material for growth.

Feeding the plants

What do your plants eat?
Baked bean butties?
Are you sure?
Don't plants eat anything?

What you will need
This sheet and a pencil.

What to do
The school holidays were starting.
'What shall we do about the plants, children?'
asked Miss Simkins.
'Leave them. They'll be all right,' said Adam.
'We ought to leave them some food,' said Bev.
'They will need watering,' added Chris.
'They will need light AND water,' said Debra.

What to record
Who was right?
Write a note to one
of the other children
telling them why
they are wrong.

Growing beansprouts

Here's an experiment you can eat.
But first you've got to grow it. You get something for nothing – or do you?

What you will need
Some mung beans.
A glass jam jar (CARE!).
A kitchen towel.
An elastic band.

What to do
Put the mung beans in the jar and add water.
Soak the beans overnight.
Pour the water away, but leave the inside of the jar – and the beans – damp.
Stretch the towel over the mouth of the jar with an elastic band.
Put the jar in a warm cupboard. If the jar dries out, open it and add a little water.

What to record
Observe and record changes in the beans.
After a couple of days, put the jar on the windowsill and observe and record.
When your enquiry is over, you can eat the bean shoots, raw in salad, or lightly cooked.

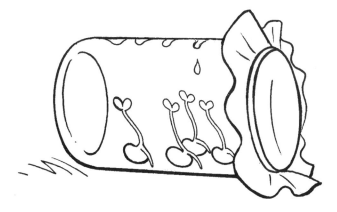 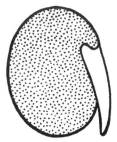

6   What makes our heart beat faster?

What children may think

Many children believe that the body is a bag containing a mass of organs, food and blood. All this is churned about inside. Blood is inconvenient, because it leaks out when you cut yourself. But it moves around, carrying food and oxygen – and possibly takes away waste, too – though this is usually lost through two handy holes when we go to the toilet.

What you may think

You may wonder why this is the only investigation you can do with the human body at primary school. The reason is simple: other investigations on the human body are either impractical, immoral or downright dangerous. But children can take their pulse rate before and after exercise, and usually notice the difference.

But there's a problem. You may think it's easy to take a pulse rate. But if you've tried getting it from a wrist you will know how difficult it is. The technique is to use fingertips and to feel between the bone of the wrist. But a more effective way is to take the pulse from the temples, or from the neck. In both places a pulse can be felt more clearly. Remember to relate that pulse to the beats of the heart or your children will think that the two are separate.

The accepted science

When we exercise our muscles need more energy, and that energy is released from our food through respiration. Our muscles need the raw materials of respiration – food and oxygen. Waste carbon dioxide will be produced. The body needs to be rid of this so the blood system takes it away.

When the exercise is over our body begins to recover. Pulse rate falls to resting rate. The speed of this recovery is one measure of fitness.

The photocopy sheets

1 Hassan's training. The graph shows that:

At the beginning of his exercise Hassan's heart rate is 40 beats/min.
Then he runs for half an hour. His heart rate rises to 80 beats/min.
Then he rests for half an hour. His heart rate falls to 45 beats/min.
Then he runs for an hour. At the end, his heart rate is 90 beats/min.

Because Hassan only takes his pulse every half hour, his graph may not tell the full story. His heart rate may rise very quickly. Then it may level off for a time.

2 Test yourself.

Ensure that the children are finding the pulse correctly – and that it is the subject's pulse and not their own. Children who do not do normal PE exercises should not take part. The speed of recovery of resting heart rate is one – but not the only – measure of fitness.

Some more activities

The activity can be varied in different ways. A swimming pool investigation will show who is water-fit. Some children recover better from explosive exercise, like racquet games, others from sustained activity.

Learning outcomes

Know that the heart pumps blood round the body and is affected by exercise and rest.

Hassan's training

Do you have training programme?
Hassan does. It helps to keep him fit.

What you will need
This sheet and a pencil.

What to do
Hassan is a keen athlete.
Every day he trains to improve his running.
He takes his pulse every half hour as he trains.

Look at this graph. It shows Hassan's heart rate over two hours.
What do you think he is doing?

What to record
At the beginning of his exercise Hassan's heart rate is _____.

Then he _____ for half an hour. His heart rate rises to _____.

Then he _____ for half an hour. His heart rate falls to _____.

Then he _____ for an hour. At the end, his heart rate is _____.

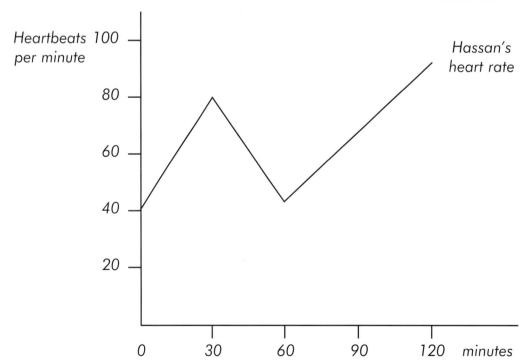

Test Yourself

Maybe your heart thumps when you are in trouble.
But it also behaves differently when you are doing exercise.

What you will need

A clock or a watch with a second hand.
A friend to help you.
SAFETY! DO NOT do more exercise than is safe for you.

What to do

1 Ask your friend to count your heart beats for 15 seconds. They can find your pulse on your wrist – or easier, on your temples (the sides of your forehead) or your throat.
2 Exercise for a minute. You might run, or jump up and down, or step up onto a PE bench.
3 Ask your friend to count your heart beats again for 15 seconds.
4 Now sit still for a minute.
5 Ask your friend to count your heart beats for 15 seconds.

What to record

Record your heart beats at different times. You might draw a graph like the one on Hassan's training.

7 How does water get up the plant?

Key Stage 2
National Curriculum
reference: Sc2, 3a,
3b, 3c

What children may think

Plants need water. They mostly get it from the ground. They suck it up through their roots. It gets to their leaves. I don't quite know what they do with it then ...

What you may think

You may not be sure why plants need so much water. You would be right to think that some of it is used for photosynthesis, of course. But a lot is transpired – lost through holes in the leaves. The plant needs to do this because it's existence (and indirectly, ours) depends upon gas exchange – the loss of oxygen and the absorption of carbon dioxide. This takes place through these holes. Then water is needed for the cells to stay turgid. When they lose water, the plant wilts.

The water rises through fine tubes called xylem. A big oak tree lifts and loses around a hundred gallons of water every day.

The accepted science

Three processes combine to lift the water through the plant.

The first is capillarity. This is the extraordinary ability of water to sneak up a dishcloth slung over the edge of a sink and then to drip all over the floor. Liquid naturally rises in thin tubes or through absorbent materials.

The second is the result of water being absorbed into the cells of the roots. Because each one is full of liquid and is surrounded by a thin membrane, they draw in water from outside. This process is called osmosis.

Finally, the leaves do draw water up the stem by their transpiration. As water is lost, the pull of the leaves causes more water to rise from the roots.

The photocopy sheets

1 Roots and shoots.

Paul was puzzled. 'I put these leafy twigs in water, but now all the water has gone.'
His friends had their own ideas:
'The plant drank it all,' said Ann.
'Some of it evaporated into the air,' said Ben.
'Plants take up water and lose it through their leaves,' said Carol.
'Carol and Ben are both right,' said Dave.
Dave is completely correct.

2 Up the stem. This is a popular activity demonstrating how water rises up a stem. Pictures should show the tubes in the stem where the water rises.

Some more activities

You can use ink as above to colour white flowers blue. Flower petals are modified leaves. Not having green pigment, white flowers show the coloured water well.

Learning outcomes

Know that water needed by the plant is drawn from the soil by the root and transported through the plant.

Roots and shoots

Why do you need to water plants?
What are they doing with it all?

What you will need
This paper and a pencil.

What to do
Paul was puzzled. 'I put these leafy twigs in water, but now all the water has gone.'
His friends had their own ideas:
'The plant drank it all,' said Ann.
'Some of it evaporated into the air,' said Ben.
'Plants take up water and lose it through their leaves,' said Carol.
'Carol and Ben are both right,' said Dave.
Who was right?

What to record
Who was right?
Write a note to one of the other children, saying what you think of their idea.

Up the stem

What colour do you like your flowers?
If you start with a white one, you can have a flower any colour you like.

What you will need

A jar of water.
Some ink.
A cut flower or celery stick.
A sharp knife, used by an adult.

What to do

Put some inky water in the pot.
Ask an adult to cut a fresh end on the
flower stem or celery stick.
Put the flower or celery stick in the water.
Leave it for a day.
Ask an adult to cut the stem across.
Look at the cut ends.

What to record

Draw what you saw when you cut the stem or stick across.
Explain what you think is happening.

8   How do you use a key?

Key Stage 2
National Curriculum
reference: Sc2, 4a, 4

What children may think

The word 'key' has so many different uses (more if you include the like-sounding 'quay'), and it can be confusing to ask children to 'use a key to sort these animals or plants'.

What you may think

You will have used a key at some time. Branching keys are popular to find a route through a problem. You will even find them in advertisements; a recent one in a car ad asked you a series of questions to help you find the model for you, and the way to finance it. 'Do you want to spread the payments over a long period?' and 'Do you want three or five doors?' were among the questions.

You may have used the huge keys that appear in flora and bird books. But a key need not be as complicated as this.

The accepted science

A branching key asks a series of questions – often with yes or no answers – which gradually bring you closer to identifying an unknown.

A simple key for most living things, for example, might ask you if your find was an animal or a plant. If you decided it was an animal, it might then go on to ask if it had a backbone. If you said it had, then the next route might take you to fur, feathers, scales or a smooth skin. Well, you knew it was a bird, so there wasn't much point to that – but other keys can help you to identify the plants on the school field or the animals in the pond.

The photocopy sheets

1 How do you use a key? Children are asked to use a branching key to identify some common minibeasts. They should understand the importance of the yes or no questions each branch.

2 Make your own key: Ask them to devise a key to identify fruit and vegetables – although you might have other objects to use. Ensure that they look at all the objects, not just one. It is very easy to ask a question that isolates a single fruit: 'Is it long, yellow and curved?', harder to ask one that divides the group.

Some more activities

There are keys in many text books and work sheets. You can differentiate between simple keys – my friends, cars in the staff car park – and complex ones – wildflowers, for example.

Learning outcomes

Know how to make a branching key, and use it in identifying and assigning to a group.

Read this key

There are many living things around us. Some of them are hard to identify. A branching key will help. It will tell you what a plant or animal is – as long as you answer the questions correctly.

What you will need
This sheet and a pencil.

What to do
Look at this key.
It is used to name common minibeasts.
Try it.

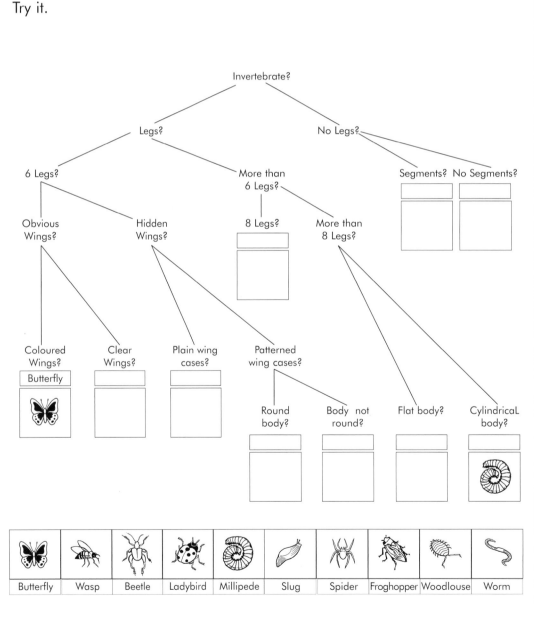

Make you own key

Now's your chance. You can make your own key to sort some fruit and vegetables. You'll know what they all are, so it should be easy.

This looks easy. You know the different fruit and vegetables. But suppose someone had never seen them before. Would your key help them?

What you will need
Some fruit or vegetables.
A large sheet of paper.

What to do
Branching keys work because at each branch in the key there is a yes or no question.

1 Look at your vegetables.
Think of a single question that will divide them into two large groups.
It might be 'Is it green?'.
2 Write this question on the sheet.
3 Divide the vegetables into two groups – green and not green.
4 Now think of a second question.
It might be 'Is it round?'.
5 Write this question on, and go on until you have divided all the vegetables and can use the key to name every one.

9 Why do green plants start food chains?

Key Stage 2
National Curriculum
reference: Sc2, 5a, 5b

What children may think

Children have very little idea of the delicate pyramid that means that even a lion cannot exist unless its prey animals eat plants. They may believe that, given enough antelope, the lions would never starve – and they'd be right; but antelope have to eat something, and they have to survive on green plants with their magical ability to harness the power of the Sun.

What you may think

You might expect food chains to be very long. Most aren't – only four or five steps even if you count in the Sun.

So a chain might go Sun $\longrightarrow$ Green plant $\longrightarrow$ Herbivore $\longrightarrow$ Carnivore $\longrightarrow$ Possibly a second carnivore.

But why start with a green plant?

The accepted science

Green plants are almost unique in their ability to harness the energy of the Sun and produce their own food. No animal can do that, and so green plants always start the chain. Carnivores cannot (usually) digest vegetable food (although some pet owners give their animals vegetarian cat food with, it is reputed, very smelly results) and so they must eat herbivores, which act as unwitting go-betweens.

Almost all food chains start with a green plant. But there are some astonishing bacteria that do not need the Sun; they are able to make food from the products of deep sea sulphur eruptions and other vile sources. Fortunately, we don't have to eat them.

The photocopy sheets

1 Food chains.

Sun ⟶ fruit from green plant ⟶ mouse ⟶ eagle

Sun ⟶ grass ⟶ rabbit ⟶ fox

Sun ⟶ pondweed ⟶ tadpole ⟶ pike

Sun ⟶ seaweed ⟶ periwinkle ⟶ seagull

2 Drawing a food web.

There are many possible connections. Children may not know that (for example) hawks will eat baby rabbits or foxes or frogs. Arrows drawn on the food web should run from food to stomach. Ultimately, arrows from green plants should come from the Sun.

Some more activities

Many natural history pictures offer opportunities for finding food webs and chains. Food chains including humans are interesting too.

Learning outcomes

Know that plants harness the Sun's energy and are eaten by animals as part of a food chain.

Why do green plants start food chains?

Food chains

*The Sun is out, the sky is blue – and a good thing too. Without the Sun,
the Earth would quickly run out of energy.*

What you will need
This sheet and a pencil.

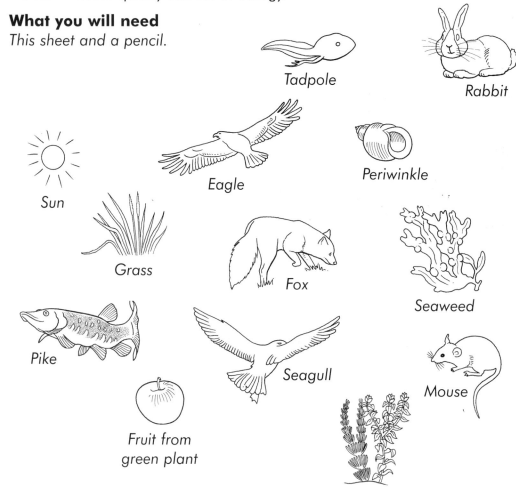

What to do
These food chains have become jumbled up.
Put them in the right order.

Eagle	mouse	fruit from green plant	Sun
Rabbit	grass	fox	Sun
Sun	pike	pond weed	tadpole
Seaweed	periwinkle	seagull	Sun

What to record
Write the food chains in the correct order.
*Draw arrows in the food chains so that they run from one thing
to the stomach of another.*

Drawing a food web

Will foxes eat frogs?
Yes, they will – and food chains can link together to make food webs.

What you will need
A pencil and this sheet.

What to do
Look at this picture.
Many food chains are possible.
Draw them in as arrows.
Draw links between them.
You have drawn a food web.

10   Are all micro-organisms germs?

Key Stage 2
National Curriculum
reference: Sc2, 5f

What children may think

Given the chance most children would eliminate all micro-organisms from the Earth – bringing it to a very early demise (see why below). This is because they have been taught that the tiny living things we can't see are all germs, that live in dirt and bring disease and infection. They associate germs with insanitary conditions and may have the idea that germs float about; small lightweight messengers of death and destruction.

What you may think

You will certainly have wider experience of micro-organisms than that. You may know of the importance of yeasts in baking bread and fermenting alcoholic drinks; you may know how important micro-organisms are in the process of making silage – a form of 'pickled grass'. You may even be aware of the use of micro-organisms in making many modern foods like meat substitutes.

Micro-organisms have both a damaging and a beneficial role.

The accepted science

If all the world's micro-organisms were eliminated, the world would come to a speedy standstill. Humans, unable to digest their food, would die up to their necks in undecayed waste. Because micro-organisms (bugs) are essential to many of our body processes and live both in and on us in huge numbers. A really hot chicken tikka will wipe out many of the bacteria in our stomach, replacing them with a fresh, more curry-tolerant flora.

Bacteria and other micro-organisms break down every form of human waste, returning it to the cycle without which life would end. Some are harmful, of course, and they cause disease and infection. But most are beneficial to us in many ways.

The industry of biotechnology which will expand massively in this new millennium, is based on the exploitation of micro-organisms.

The photocopy sheets

1 Micro-organisms. The use of micro-organisms for making silage, making yoghurt and raising bread are all beneficial.

2 Growing yeasts.

After a few minutes, the yeast mixture began to bubble. (Carbon dioxide is being given off.)
After half an hour the bottle was filling or full of foam. (The carbon dioxide in the yeast mixture.)
After several hours, the bubbling stopped.
We think this is because the yeast is growing and dividing, using the sugar as food. It produces carbon dioxide and alcohol as waste products. Eventually, the alcohol becomes so strong that it kills the yeast.

Some more activities

You might try a little yeast mixture under a conventional scientist's microscope. The yeast cells can be clearly seen, and children may even see them dividing. Yeast mixture is not like liver salts – it fizzes because yeast is a living thing.

Learning outcomes

Know that micro-organisms can be both beneficial and harmful.

Micro-organisms

Did you know that micro-organisms can be really useful? They help make pickled grass – that farm animals eat in winter and that they find tasty and satisfying.

What you will need
This sheet and your pencil.

What to do
Look at the picture. It shows some of the ways in which micro-organisms affect our lives.
Put each picture number in the table below.
Write the word 'beneficial' – meaning good; or 'harmful' next to each one.

What to record

	Benificial	**Harmful**
Picture 1		
Picture 2		
Picture 3		
Picture 4		
Picture 5		

What the pictures show
Bacteria can get into cuts in our skin
Bacteria help make silage – pickled grass – for animals to eat in the winter.
Bacteria sneezed into the air can make us ill
Bacteria turns milk to yoghurt
Yeasts make bread rise

Growing yeasts

Yeast makes bread rise. It brews beer and ferments wine. It's great stuff. But can it really be alive?

What you will need

Some baking yeast – dried or fresh.
A small bottle.
Some cotton wool.
A teaspoon of sugar.
Warm water – the same temperature as your hand.

What to do

Put the yeast and sugar in the bottle and half-fill it with warm water.
Put your thumb over the bottle top and shake it gently to dissolve the sugar.
Plug the bottle top with cotton wool and leave it in a warm place.

What to record

Fill the spaces:

After a few minutes the yeast mixture began to _____.

After half an hour the bottle was _____.

After several hours, _____.

We think this is because_____.

Part 3

Sc3 Materials and their properties.

11   What makes this jumper warm?

Key Stage 2
National Curriculum
reference: Sc3, 1b

What children may think

'Put on your warm jumper; it's cold outside.' No wonder children grow up with the idea that jumpers themselves are 'warm'. Yet a wool jumper is no warmer than a cotton shirt or a nylon nightie. Yet there are clearly clothes that are better suited to cold days and to warm; and children may have observed that thick, woolly, close-fitting clothes are best for cold days, and light, loose clothes for warm.

What you may think

But surely some clothes do feel warmer to the touch than others? They certainly do. And some surfaces – metal, ceramics, some plastics – can feel cool on a hot day and really cold on a cool one. But that is because of their insulation properties (see below). We judge temperature in relation to our own body heat. Some surfaces which are good conductors of heat – like metals – conduct our body heat away. They feel cold to the touch. Other surfaces, which are poor conductors (and good insulators) do not conduct our body heat away so efficiently, and therefore feel warm to the touch. There are even some surfaces – like expanded polystyrene – that reflect our body heat back to us so that they may feel warmer than we are.

The accepted science

The warmth in a warm jumper comes from you. Your body heat is retained better by good insulators. Wool works well as an insulator because its loose fibres trap air. And air is a good insulator. When you slip on a jumper, you warm the air trapped in it. This blanket of warm air surrounds you and keeps you warm. Thin, loose cottons are not such good insulators. They don't trap a thick layer of air as wool does. You feel cool in them.

The photocopy sheets

1 Cold days. The words describing 'warm' winter clothing should be underlined. They retain body heat best.

2 Keeping warm. A bottle wrapped in a good thermal insulator should stay warmest longest. It reduces the loss of heat.

Some more activities

Collecting and testing examples of winter clothing. But be sensitive to children who for cultural and other reasons do not necessarily wear appropriate clothes for winter days.

Learning outcomes

Know that some materials are good insulators.

Cold days

What would you pick for an icy day – swimming trunks or a fleece? Why the fleece? What does a fleece do that swimming trunks don't?

What you will need
This sheet and a pencil.

What to do
*Choose the words that describe the best clothes for a cold day.
Then explain why you would wear clothes like these.*

What to record
Underline the words that describe the best clothes for a cold day:

light   heavy

woolly   fleecy

thick   thin   thick

cotton   furry

I would wear clothes like these because:

Keeping warm

'Put your warm jumper on before you go out!' But can a jumper be warm?
And if it is, just what fuel is it using?

What you will need
Some plastic bottles – small pop bottles are best.
Warm water from the tap.
Materials including fabrics – all the same size.
Elastic bands.
One or more thermometers.

What to do
Fill each bottle with warm water.
Check that all the temperatures are the same.
Wrap each bottle in a piece of material and
secure it with an elastic band.
Take the temperature in each bottle every
ten minutes and record the changes.

What to record
You could write your results or graph them. They will make a line
graph with the time on the x-axis and the temperature on the y-axis.
Each bottle will have its own line.

Now complete this sentence:

The bottle wrapped in _____ stayed warmest longest. I think
this is because

12   Why isn't flour a liquid?

Key Stage 2
National Curriculum
reference: Sc3, 1e

What children may think

We've learned that there are solids, liquids and gases. Solids are hard and rigid. Liquids pour. Gases are very puzzling – here one moment, gone the next. They don't weigh anything of course. In fact, if you put gas in something it can actually appear to lose weight.

But some materials are funny – powders especially. We've learned that flour is a solid, yet it pours like a liquid. What is it? Is it halfway between the two?'

What you may think

Solids, liquids and gases can be confusing. That's because the rules are sometimes difficult to apply, and also because – as in so much of science – there are in-betweens that don't fit the pattern – and even downright impossibilities – is glass really a liquid?

The accepted science

Solids are materials that can't be easily compressed – and even tiny flour particles fit that pattern. Liquids do pour. They also take the shape of the container you put them in. But so do sugar, salt, sand and flour. The difference is that poured liquids form a flat top, where poured solids usually make a cone – like a volcano. You would be very surprised if you ran a bath only to find that it came to a point in the middle.

Gases do have weight. A blown-up balloon weighs more than a flat one. But some gases are less dense than air – including hydrogen and helium – and hot air is less dense than cold. So gas balloons and hot air balloons rise. Gases fill the space available to them.

The photocopy sheets

1 Solids, liquids and gases.

carbon dioxide
(oil)
oxygen
[salt]
[sawdust]
(vinegar)

2 Changing state. The children should recognise that the same water can exist in all three states. The point about steam and water vapour is difficult and goes against everyday use of the words – but a gas is above boiling point, and so what we usually call steam is water vapour.

Adult supervision is essential for this activity.

Some more activities

Demonstrate gases with an air freshener which fills the space available in time. Burn candles, with safety precautions. You can see solid, liquid and gaseous wax.

Learning outcomes

Know that there are solids, liquids and gases and explain the differences between them.

Solids, liquids and gases

Flour pours. Flour runs. Flour slurps into jars and trickles through your fingers. So why isn't flour a liquid?

What you will need
This sheet and a pencil.

What to do
Look at these names of materials:

carbon dioxide

sawdust

vinegar

salt

oil

oxygen

What to record

Underline *the gases.*

Ring *the liquids.*

[Bracket] *the solids.*

Now think of one more gas, liquid and solid, and mark those too.

Changing state

Can you destroy water? Suppose you make it really hot or cold? Surely that will finish it off? Death to water!

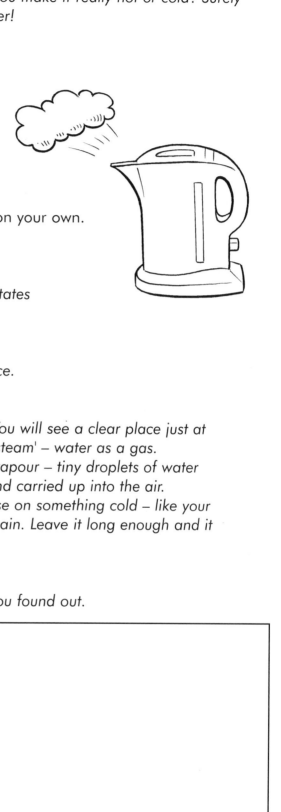

What you will need
Some water.
An ice tray and refrigerator.
With adult help only, a kettle.

SAFETY! DO NOT do this activity on your own.
An adult must handle the kettle.

What to do
Ice can exist on Earth in all three states
solid, liquid and gas.

Your water is liquid.
Freeze some. It will become solid ice.
Put some in a kettle.
Ask an adult to boil it for you.
As it boils watch the kettle spout. You will see a clear place just at the spout. This is the area of true 'steam' – water as a gas.
Then you will see clouds of water vapour – tiny droplets of water below the boiling point of water and carried up into the air.
The droplets of water may condense on something cold – like your ice tray – and form liquid water again. Leave it long enough and it will freeze.

What to record
Describe what you did and what you found out.

13   Why don't ice cubes sink?

Key Stage 2
National Curriculum
reference: Sc3, 2b,
2e, 2f

What children may think

It's hard to believe that water, ice and steam are all the same material. And ice is funny stuff. It's hard and cold, and you might think that when you put it in water, it would sink. At least, that's what children often expect.

What you may think

It's all very confusing. Just when you think you've got the hang of this solids/liquids business – and you know that solids are denser than the liquids they are made from, smaller in volume and sink. Along comes water to break all those rules.

And what about steam and water vapour? Isn't that cloudy stuff in the bathroom steam? Doesn't it make condensation all over the mirror?

The accepted science

Water exists in three states – solid, liquid and gas – ice, water and steam. But water is unique in that when it freezes, it actually gets bigger than the liquid from which it froze. We've all seen this in frozen milk bottles with a plug of frozen milk emerging from the top; in ice cubes that bulge out of the tray; if we're unlucky, then in pipes that have frozen and burst. This frozen water, ice, is also denser than the liquid it is made from. And a good thing too. Ice forms on the top of ponds, not on the bottom, and unless the entire pond freezes through, fish can happily swim about under the ice. If this were not so, then it is unlikely that life would have begun in water. A cold snap would have finished it off.

Water forms steam when it is above 100°C. So real steam – water gas – is actually invisible. You might not see it at the spout of a kettle. As soon as its temperature falls below boiling point, it forms water droplets, and these clouds of droplets fill the bathroom when you run a hot bath. We call this steam. But actually it is water vapour – droplets of water floating on air. When it reaches a cold surface it condenses – a verb describing the process of condensation, not a noun – and becomes liquid water again.

The photocopy sheets

1 A chilly problem. The children are asked to explain:

a) A skater on an outdoor pond.
b) An icebreaker cutting its way through frozen waves.
c) A fisherman fishing through a hole in the ice.
d) A child fallen through thin ice.

They should be able to explain that ice is frozen water, that ice floats on water, that it is possible to walk on thick ice, that ice can melt and break. They will have other ideas.

2 Ice balloon. You can make one by filling a long balloon with water, tying it up, putting it in a plastic bag (in case it bursts) and leaving it in the freezer. When it has frozen, peel off the balloon.

The children can explore the balloon in many different ways. They will have first hand experience of the behaviour of a large lump of ice.

Some more activities

Explore what food colours do to ice; where is the best place to keep ice, and where it melts fastest. If you have ICT and a temperature probe, you can record the temperature at which ice melts – with and without salt.

Learning outcomes

Know that water exists as solid, liquid and gas and explain the difference between them all.

A chilly problem

Strange stuff, ice. Made of water, but floats on water.

What you will need
*Look at these pictures.
They all show icy scenes.*

What to do
*Explain what is happening in each
picture.*

What to record
Picture 1. How can the skater move around on water?
Picture 2. Why does the ship need to break its way through the sea?
Picture 3. How can the fisherman walk over the fish?
Picture 4: What's happened here – and why?

SAFETY! Remember that ice on ponds and streams can be
dangerous.

Ice balloon

Ice sank the Titanic. Now you can explore an iceberg.

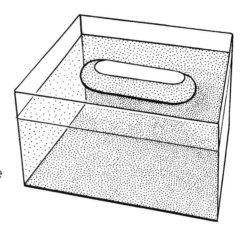

What you will need
An ice balloon. You can make one by filling a long balloon with water, tying it up, putting it in a plastic bag (in case it bursts) and leaving it in the freezer. When it has frozen, peel off the balloon.
A bowl of water.
Salt.
Food colours.

What to do
Peel the ice balloon and put it in the water.
Explore it, and record your observations.

What to record
What do you observe:

* *when the iceberg is in the water?*
* *when you put salt on it?*
* *when you put hot or cold water on it?*
* *when you put food colour on it?*

Record how the iceberg melts.
What other tests can you do?

14   How do you separate salt and sand?

Key Stage 2
National Curriculum
reference: Sc3, 3a,
3b, 3c, 3d, 3e

What children may think

When I add sugar to my tea, it just disappears. You see the same thing when you add salt to water; first it's there, then it's not. The water won't weigh any more with the salt in it; it's just disappeared. You could go on adding salt if you liked; it would just go on filling the spaces.

What you may think

Surely the salt has to go somewhere? What do you think? You may answer that 'I guess it fills spaces in the water until there are no more to be filled; then it begins to accumulate at the bottom. I think the water would weigh more. And, of course, the water will eventually fill the container and overflow'.

The accepted science

When you add a solid that will dissolve to a liquid, it begins by filling the spaces between the particles of liquid. Rather like a cinema with a fixed number of seats, the liquid will take so many arrivals before it is full. When it is full, the liquid can take no more and is said to be saturated. The excess - like disappointed film-goers - is rejected and it sinks to the bottom. Strangely, the level actually falls at first.

But some materials like sand don't dissolve. They may sink to the bottom of the liquid, or, if they are low density, they may sit in mid-water or in suspension.

If you put the liquid through a filter, the dissolved particles pass through; but large undissolved particles are netted and stay behind. If you then let the water evaporate you will be left with the dissolved solid – which may form crystals.

The photocopy sheets

1 Stones, gravel and sand. The children will need to know the correct order in which to use coarse and fine sieves.

First Gerry uses a coarse sieve to keep back all the stones.
Next Gerry uses a fine sieve to keep back all the gravel.
All the sand goes through.

They may need gravel explained as between stones and sand in grain size.

2 Salt and sand. The children are asked to separate a mixture of salt and sand. The correct technique is as follows:

Mix the salt and sand with water.
Put the filter paper in the funnel.
Carefully pour the mixture through the filter funnel into a container.
Save the sand in the filter funnel.
Dry out the sand.
Leave the liquid that came through the funnel.
Allow it to evaporate.
Collect the salt crystals.
Collect the sand.

Learning outcomes

I know that I can get back solids that don't dissolve by filtering; and dissolved solids by evaporation.

Stones, gravel and sand

*It can take a long time to separate things that have been mixed.
Imagine being given a barrowful of earth – and being told to
take all the stones out!*

What you will need
Your pencil and this sheet.

What to do
*Look at these pictures.
Gerry the gardener has been
asked to make piles of stones, gravel and sand.
How will he separate them?
Explain his clever plan!*

What to record
*First Gerry uses a _____ _____ to keep back all the
_____ .*

*Next Gerry uses a _____ _____ to keep back all the
_____.*

All the _____ goes through.

Use these words:
sieve
coarse
sand
fine
gravel
stones

Salt and sand

Disaster. There's sand in the salt!
How can you separate them?

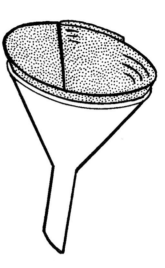

What you will need
Three containers.
A funnel.
Filter paper, blotting paper or soft towel.
Salt mixed with sand.
Water.

What to do
Follow these instructions.
Unfortunately, they've got jumbled up.

First, put them in the right order:

Allow it to evaporate.
Carefully pour the mixture through the filter funnel into a container.
Collect the salt crystals.
Collect the sand.
Dry out the sand.
Leave the liquid that came through the funnel.
Mix the salt and sand with water.
Put the filter paper in the funnel.
Save the sand in the filter funnel.

What to record
Record what you did. Try putting the instructions in the right order.

Part 4

Sc4 Physical processes

15   How do you draw a circuit?

What children may think

'My teacher has asked me to draw my circuit. I'd rather draw something interesting – like a horse, I'm good at horses. But I'd better get on with it. The only interesting bit really is the battery. It's blue and red with shiny bits at the end. How do you spell the name on it? I must get that right. There, that's better. There are some wires too, and a bulb, but I won't put them in'.

What you may think

You may believe that a picture of a circuit really should show where everything belongs. It's important that the wires start from the battery and go back to it. The order of the bits (battery, switch, lamp) really matters.

The accepted science

A circuit diagram is a schematic of what you have made or want to make. It is not a picture of the circuit any more than the London Underground Map is a picture of the tube lines. Just as stations are represented by dashes or circles, so the components in the circuit are represented diagrammatically. It can be read by anyone who knows the code, and the actual distances and directions of the wires are not important. Only the order – and sometimes the orientation – of the components matter. Some devices (buzzers and light emitting diodes, for example) only work when the correct side of them is connected to the correct side of the battery. They are said to be polarised.

The photocopy sheets

1 Read these symbols

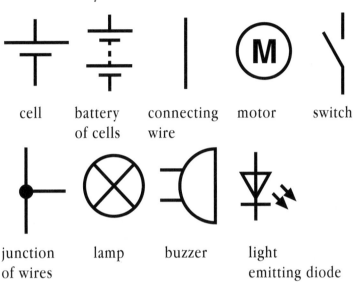

cell   battery   connecting   motor   switch
         of cells   wire

junction   lamp   buzzer   light
of wires   emitting diode

2 Your circuit diagram. Children are asked to draw, read and possibly construct from a circuit diagram.

Note that both LEDs and buzzers are polarised. They will only work in one direction in the circuit. The buzzer may be colour-coded for positive and negative. The LED has a longer + (positive) leg.

Some more activities

Other possible ways of using the symbols would be as matching cards – picture to definition – or to make your own diagrams as differentiated work cards for children.

Learning outcomes

Know that a circuit diagram represents a circuit using symbols other people will recognise.

Read these symbols

When we write we use letters that everyone recognises.
When scientists write, they use symbols that everyone knows.
Here are some of those symbols. How many do you know?

What you will need
A pencil and this sheet.

What to do
Here are some symbols to use in drawing circuit diagrams.
Next to each, write what it represents.

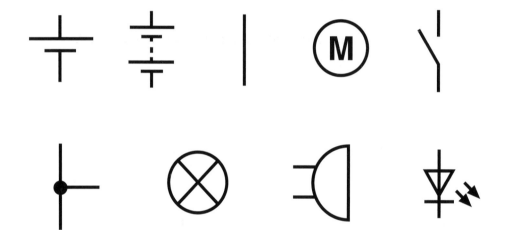

battery of cells

motor

cell

connecting wire

buzzer

switch   junction of wires

lamp   light emitting diode

Draw your own circuit

Can you draw a circuit using the correct symbols that your friend can use as a plan? Can they read it – and build the circuit – and will it work?

What you will need
This sheet and a pencil.

What to do
Here are the common symbols for the components in an electrical circuit.
Use some of them to draw a circuit of your own.
Give the circuit to a friend.
Ask them what it means.
If you have the components, use them to make and use the circuit.

Symbols for:

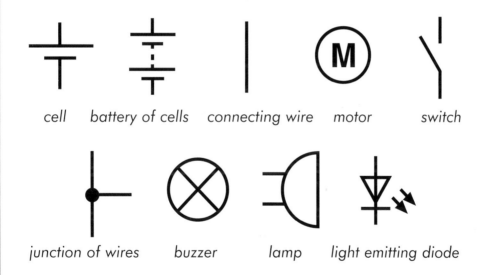

| cell | battery of cells | connecting wire | motor | switch |

| junction of wires | buzzer | lamp | light emitting diode |

What to record
Your circuit diagram.

16   Which metals are magnetic?

Key Stage 2
National Curriculum
reference: Sc4, 2a

What children may think

Magnets bring out real excitement from children. 'I've got a magnet! It sticks to metals! It picked up lots of paper-clips. It works on the door hinge. I'm going to try it on the door handle. Whoops! I've dropped it. It didn't stick. That's funny; I'm sure this door handle is metal. Let's try the tap. Whoops! I've dropped it again. It didn't stick to the tap either. I don't think this magnet works properly ...'

What you may think

You may think that all metals are magnetic. A magnet will be attracted to all of them. Your magnets don't work because they've been rattling round in that box for too long. You should have put them away with keepers. And anyway, these children keep dropping them; and I'm sure I've heard somewhere that it's bad for magnets to drop them. 'Right! We'll stop now, girls and boys. Put the magnets back in the box. Don't throw them in!'

The accepted science

Some metals are strongly magnetic. Iron and its derivatives are. So are cobalt and nickel. Other materials – including other metals – behave differently with magnets. They may not be magnetic.

When you make a magnet you turn all the tiny magnetic particles inside it – which are usually facing randomly – to face the same way. It's like a football crowd all turning to face the goal. As a result, the particles at each end of the magnet are aligned – all faces at one end, all backs at the other – and their combined magnetic force results in the two poles. Magnets attract some metals. But only a magnet can repel another magnet.

When you put the magnets away in pairs with keepers, the magnetic force is held in the ring that results and the magnets last longer. Dropping magnets shakes the aligned particles out of order, and the magnets lose their magic power ...

The photocopy sheets

1 Magnetic materials. Children are asked to predict whether some given classroom objects are magnetic:

* a metal door handle – probably won't be; mostly aluminium alloy
* a water tap – probably won't be – mostly zinc alloy (even a stainless steel sink, if you have one, will probably not be magnetic, as stainless steel is non-magnetic steel)
* a stapler – will be; made of steel
* a plastic tidy box/tray – won't be
* a pencil – won't be
* a wooden ruler – won't be
* a pile of paper clips – will be; steel
* an elastic band – won't be
* an eraser – won't be
* a food can used to store pencils – will be, but not because it is 'tin', the tin is a metal coating on a steel can

Children will learn that not all metals are magnetic.

2 Testing metals. The children are asked to choose a safe object to test, predict whether it will be magnetic, record whether it is magnetic or not, and say why they got their result. They will find that only objects containing iron and steel are magnetic – but note the points on stainless steel and 'tins' above. Finally, ask them to test another magnet. They will find that magnets will attract each other, but the difference between a magnet and any other piece of metal is that a magnet can repel another magnet.

Some more activities

There are innumerable magnet games – 'dancing' metal objects on card over a magnet, paper clip chains, moving metal filings (in a plastic box for safety), fishing games and so on. A magnetic game is a nice technology challenge.

Learning outcomes

Know that not all metals are magnetic, and that magnets repel each other.

Magnetic materials

What things are magnetic? Suppose you were to test the things on this page. Which ones would the magnet stick to – and why?

What you will need
This sheet and a pencil.

What to do
Look at these pictures. They show objects that you might find around your classroom. If you think they would be magnetic, draw a magnet stuck on them.

What to record
Which of these objects might be magnetic?
Why do you say that?

Testing metals

What you will need

A magnet.
This sheet to record your results.

SAFETY! DO NOT TEST ANYTHING ELECTRICAL WITH YOUR
MAGNET – SWITCHES, PLUGS.
Don't test watches either, since the magnet will damage them.

What to do

Choose a safe object to test.
Predict whether it will be magnetic.
Record whether it is magnetic or not.
Say why you got your result.

What to record

My Object	What I think	What I found	Why I found that

17   Why does my shadow look like me?

Key Stage 2
National Curriculum
reference: Sc4, 3b

What children may think

My shadow is very puzzling. It's not there all the time; but when it is, it looks like me – usually. Sometime it's bigger than me, or smaller than me, or longer or shorter.

Where do shadows come from? Is my shadow inside me? Does it just pop out when the Sun is shining? Or has it a life of its own, like the shadow in Peter Pan? It's all very strange.

What you may think

Shadows are cast by opaque objects. Because light travels in straight lines, shadows look like the object that blocks the light. All that is true. But I've two puzzles. Often, there are two shadows – a dark one and a lighter one surrounding it. Why is that?

And here's a strange thing. When you stand in front of a light your shadow on the wall can be bigger than you. Yet when an aeroplane flies over its shadow is exactly the same size as the plane. Why is that?

The accepted science

Light travels in straight lines. This is hard to grasp because light travels much too fast for us to experience its movement. In fact, when you turn the light on, the light fills the room in time like water from the tap. But unlike water, it takes an immeasurably short time to do it. Light travels in straight lines but children often find it easier to understand that light doesn't go round corners. They are used to this. They can hide behind things and their friends can't see them. The game would be ruined if you could see round the corner. But you can't.

But why do things have two types of shadow? The answer is that you get a totally black shadow alone when things are lit from a point – or a distant light like the Sun. Once the light is larger, the shadow is cast in two parts – a dark umbra, and a lighter surrounding penumbra where the shadow is giving way to light.

And the aeroplane shadow? Well, that is pure umbra because the Sun is so far away. And because of that distance light from the Sun is not radiating as it might from a lamp. The rays are pretty well parallel, and the shadow is the same size as the plane.

The photocopy sheets

1 Exploring shadows. Look for answers like these:

When do you get the biggest shadow? When the object is closest to the light.
When do you get the smallest shadow? When the object is closest to the wall/screen.
When do you get a deep umbra and a pale penumbra? When the light source is large, or the object is far enough away to allow light from (say) the top of the lamp to 'spill' round it.
Why is each shadow the shape of the object? Because light travels in straight lines, and shows the shape of the object that blocks it.

2 Shadow length.

The closer the pencil to the lamp, the bigger the shadow.
Why do you think this is? The light spreads out from the source. If an object is held close to the lamp its shadow expands in size with the expanding beam of light.

Some more activities

There are plenty of shadow games possible that develop experience of shadows. Try them outside on a sunny day: who can: make the most grotesque shadow? make a shadow with four legs but only two arms? make a shadow with three arms but only two legs? make a shadow with two heads? and so on.

Learning outcomes

Know that shadows are cast when light is blocked by an opaque object.

Exploring Shadows

What you will need
A safe light source – an electric torch or safe desk lamp.
Some objects to investigate.

What to do
Put the objects in front of the light source so that they cast a shadow on the wall.
Answer the questions below.

What to record
When do you get the biggest shadow?

When do you get the smallest shadow?

When do you get a deep umbra and a pale penumbra?

Why is each shadow the shape of the object?

Shadow length

As your shape changes, so does the shape of your shadow.
But when is your shadow much bigger than you?

What you will need
A safe light source – an electric torch
or a safe desk lamp.
A pencil.
A ruler.

What to do
Shine the lamp at the wall.
Hold the pencil upright
between the lamp and
the wall. Make the two
measurements below.

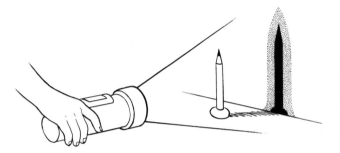

What to record
Measure the distance from the lamp to the pencil.
Measure the length of the pencil shadow.

Put your results in this table:

Distance from the lamp to the pencil	Length of the shadow

Now complete this sentence:
The closer the pencil to the lamp, the .... the shadow.
Why do you think this is?

18 Is that sound lower or higher?

Key Stage 2
National Curriculum
reference: Sc4, 3e,
3g

What children may think

Children may have problems in separating changes in volume from changes in pitch, singing or playing louder when asked to play higher and so on. This understanding needs to be learned. It's not surprising that children may have real difficulties in accounting for how sounds are made, suggesting, for example, that sound-making is a characteristic of a particular material – 'metal always makes that ringing noise'. As children get older, they may begin to relate sound production to vibration; and even to suggest that sounds are made by the surface of an object.

It doesn't help children's understanding that many vibrations are invisible.

What you may think

You may well know that sounds are made when something vibrates. But can you account for how that vibration reaches your ear? You might think that sound is transported from molecule to molecule through the air, or that it moves like some sort of breeze. Neither explanation is correct.

The accepted science

Sounds are made when objects vibrate. These high speed vibrations make pressure differences in the air that travel out in every direction like a swelling sphere. The greater the speed of the vibrations (the more there are per second) the higher the pitch of the sound; the stronger the vibrations (the greater the size of the movement) the louder the sound.

The photocopy sheets

1 Sound sources. Everyone can hear the rock singer – they can hardly miss him. This is because sound travels out from a source in all directions. If you could see the sound, it would appear to be a rapidly expanding ball.

2 Seeing the sound. The fork and string gives a remarkable sound – like church bells – because the sound is transmitted direct from the vibrating fork to your ear – there is a good sound coupling. Putting rice grains on a drum before it is tapped enables children to 'see the sound'.

Some more activities

For a demonstration of the power of sound waves, strike a tuning fork on the table and plunge it quickly into water; the surface fizzes with the energy of the vibrations.

Learning outcomes

Know that sounds are made when an object vibrates, and that faster vibrations produce higher sounds, while stronger vibrations produce louder ones.

Sound sources

So what happens when a sound is made?
Just where does the sound come from – and where does it go?

Which way does sound go?
Who can hear it – and who can't?

What you will need
A pencil and this sheet.

What to do
Look at this picture.
Draw straight arrows
from the sound source
to the people listening.

What to record
Complete this sentence: Sound travels out from a sound source ...

Seeing the sound

What you will need
An ordinary kitchen fork.
A metre of string.
A drum.
Some dry rice grains or seeds.

What to do
Tie the fork in the middle of the string.
Hold the ends of the string to your ears – NOT in them, so that the fork hangs.
Swing the fork against a table edge – and listen.

The string is vibrating with the sound made by the fork.
But you can't see the vibrations.
Use the drum and rice grains so that you can see the sound vibrations.

What to record
What did you do with the drum and the rice grains?
What did you see?

19   How do we get eclipses?

Key Stage 2
National Curriculu
reference: Sc4, 4a,
4b, 4c, 4d

What children may think

The universe is huge. We're just specks in it. There are planets everywhere. We live on one – the Earth. There's life on Earth because we've got the Sun. The Sun goes across the sky every day. The Moon does the same at night. The Moon changes shape, probably because the Sun makes the Earth's shadow on it. Then there are eclipses ...

What you may think

It's unlikely that you have a clear idea of the size of the Universe, or the relative sizes of the heavenly bodies, or the way that they move relative to each other. Few people have. The whole system is so enormous and complex. You are not helped by books that are forced to cram the whole Solar system on to a double page spread, distorting relative sizes and distances.

The accepted science

The Sun is just one of billions of stars. Despite appearances the Earth orbits the Sun, spinning on its axis as it does so. You could fit a million Earths in the Sun. The Earth's spin makes it look as if the Sun is moving. Because the Earth is angled, our bit of it faces the Sun in different ways in different seasons. It may face it directly during the summer months, or more obliquely during the winter. This means that we can be warmer or colder.

The Moon is one-sixth the size of the Earth and orbits us. Its orbit exactly matches its rotation so we only ever see one side of the Moon. But the other side is far from 'dark'. As it orbits us it may be fully lit by the Sun (full Moon) or lit from behind (New Moon). These changes cause the phases of the Moon. The Sun can throw the shadow of the Earth on the Moon, and this is called a lunar eclipse. Because the Sun's face is around 600 times the size of the Moon's, but it is 600 times as far away, the Moon can cover the Sun exactly during a solar eclipse.

The photocopy sheets

1 What do you know about space? A true/false activity that will give you an

idea of children's prior knowledge. You may be surprised. It is vital to share the correct answers with the children before moving on; many of the fallacies are commonly believed by children and adults.

The Earth, the Moon and the Sun are all spheres. True.
The Moon and the Sun are the same size. False. They are hugely different in size. You could fit a million Earths in the Sun; the Moon is one sixth the size of the Earth.
The Sun goes round the Earth. False. The Sun appears to go round the Earth because we see it moving across the sky as a result of Earth's spin.
The Moon goes round the Earth. True; once every 28 days; once a 'month'.
The Moon shines with a light of its own. False. The Moon is a ball of rock with no light of its own. Moonlight is light from the Sun reflected from the Moon.
A shadow on the Moon makes its shape seem to change. True. We call these the phases of the Moon.
The Earth is closer to the Sun in summer. False. In fact, Earth is further from the Sun in the UK summer than in the UK winter. The seasons are caused by the angle of the Sun's rays striking the Earth.

2 Model the movement. The children are asked to model the movement of Earth, Moon and Sun with balls, and then act it out. Note that:

The Earth and Moon both orbit anti-clockwise, seen from above.
To be strictly accurate, the Earth should be rotating as well as orbiting.
When modelling the Moon round the Earth near a window, the light on the 'Moon' models the phases – light full on the face for full Moon, face in shadow for new Moon and so on.

Some more activities

Children can observe the Moon using low-power binoculars, and see the 'seas' and Mountains. They must NEVER look directly at the Sun; but you can get a tiny reflected image of it using two cards. Make a pinhole in one and adjust it so that the light from the Sun passes through it and is projected onto the second card. DO NOT look up to see if you are in line with the Sun. Use your own shadow direction to judge.

Learning outcomes

Know the relative sizes, distances and movements of the Earth, Sun and Moon; and use them to explain day and night, the seasons, and the phases of the Moon.

What do you know about space?

Which is bigger, the Moon or the Sun?
They both look the same size in the sky, so how can they be different?

What you will need
This sheet and a pencil.

What to do
Read these sentences.
Say which are true and which are false – and WHY.

The Earth, the Moon and the Sun are all spheres.

The Moon and the Sun are the same size.

The Sun goes round the Earth.

The Moon goes round the Earth.

The Moon shines with a light of its own.

A shadow on the Moon makes its shape seem to change.

The Earth is closer to the Sun in summer.

Model the movement

Do you know how the Earth, Moon and Sun move?
Here's your chance to 'star' as the Sun. You can be planet Earth – or the Moon. You only have to run round in circles.

What you will need
Three balls of different sizes.
A chair.

What to do
Use the balls as the Earth, Moon and Sun. (Remember that they are very different in size – much more than your three balls!) Keep the Sun still. Move the Earth and Moon as they move in real life.
Now act the movements yourselves. One person sits in the chair as the Sun, and the others move round them.

Finally, two of you act the Earth and Moon. One sits in the chair as the Earth; the other moves round them as the Moon, KEEPING THEIR FACE TO THE EARTH. If you do this near the window, this can be the Sun.

What to record
Write down what you found out.